BALLET PHYSIQUE

WITH NOTES ON STRESSES AND INJURIES

MARGOT FONTEYN IN "LA PÉRI"   *Houston Rogers*

BALLET
PHYSIQUE

WITH NOTES ON STRESSES AND INJURIES

BY

CELIA SPARGER

M.C.S.P., C.C.P.E.,

FORMER CONSULTING PHYSIOTHERAPIST
TO THE ROYAL BALLET SCHOOL, AUTHOR
OF "ANATOMY AND BALLET" AND
"BEGINNING BALLET"

WITH A FOREWORD BY
JAMES MONAHAN

39 DRAWINGS BY PETER REVITT
AND 26 OTHER ILLUSTRATIONS

NEW YORK
THE MACMILLAN COMPANY

FIRST PUBLISHED 1958

PRINTED IN GREAT BRITAIN BY
J. W. ARROWSMITH LTD., WINTERSTOKE ROAD, BRISTOL

FOREWORD

by JAMES MONAHAN

In the young world of British ballet Celia Sparger is a special kind of pioneer. The unmapped territory of her exploration lies between the strictly medical study of physique and the purely artistic judgement of a ballet dancer's quality. It is, of course, a territory where many of the people who are concerned with ballet stray more or less haphazardly. Teachers, obviously, are interested both in their pupils' physical capabilities and in the artistic instrument which they hope these pupils will become. And when the critic or the public judges a ballet dancer's aesthetic merits or demerits that judgment makes much play with expressions about arms, feet, hands, legs and carriage. Celia Sparger's difference is that she is, at once, highly trained to observe the causes of physical strength, weakness, grace and awkwardness, has had an exceptionally long and cogent experience in applying that training to the fledgling talent of the Royal Ballet School and, in the final issue, is less interested in physique than in artistry. To find something of this blended outlook in one person is not rare at all. But what is most rare is to find it in so intense a form—so intense, indeed, that it amounts to an almost unique qualification for the task of helping to discover what child is likely to become a fine dancer and what are the particular physical difficulties which need to be overcome if the promising pupil is not to fall by the wayside.

It will be obvious, therefore, that Celia Sparger writes primarily for the teacher. She is the teacher's teacher, one whose exploratory reflections are pregnant with invaluable advice to those who train dancers. Where others have scratched the surface she has tried to dig methodically; and her advice is all the more valuable because she, more than anyone, is aware that the digging has only just begun.

But if she writes for the teacher she also writes for anyone who not only "knows what he likes" in ballet but also wants to understand why a given dancer has certain attributes. Celia Sparger herself is passionately concerned to understand "the why of it". Yet she is very conscious that, after all the careful, experienced assessment of physical evidence, there remains, in the end, that mystery—a dancer's art.

AUTHOR'S NOTE

In preparing this book for publication I have received much help and useful advice from many friends and I would like particularly to acknowledge my gratitude to Miss Ursula Moreton and to my colleagues and friends at the Royal Ballet School, and the Royal Academy of Dancing, and to Mr. Peter Revitt, Mr. James Monahan and Mr. Cyril Swinson. My special thanks are due to the students of the Royal Academy of Dancing and of the Royal Ballet School, who posed for the photographs on pages 21, 24, 25, 30, 31, 32 and 35.

C.S.

CONTENTS

PART 1
BALLET AND PHYSIQUE

PART 2
INJURIES: PREVENTION AND CURE

INTRODUCTION

IT has been the lot of the author during the past ten years to examine some hundreds of children, all hoping to be the future ballerina of her (or her parents') dreams, children who have passed their dancing auditions and medical examination, but for whom a final verdict as to suitability from the point of view of physique and structure has been required; and also for many years previously, to have treated the mishaps and injuries which are inevitable in the arduous profession of the ballet dancer. The material therefore which follows is drawn from the result of this experience.

More than one well-known and well-loved dancer of today has been heard to say "If I had to go up for an audition today I would never be accepted." This is not likely to be true in fact, for real artistry and the gift of movement will always weigh heavily in the balance against physical imperfections; but it is true that more attention is given today than formerly to the importance of starting with a good foundation—the structure of the body. This is all the more necessary in that multitudes of children now learn ballet from a young age and a surprising number of very diverse shapes and sizes present themselves at auditions, apparently very little thought having been given to their physical suitability, childish talent presumably being deemed capable of over-riding all alse. But between childish talent and even the back row of the *corps-de-ballet* there is a stretch of years, full of hazards and unforeseeable factors even for the most physically perfect, whilst for those with structural difficulties to overcome the outlook is even more uncertain. Perhaps fortunately, we have no statistics showing the percentage of trainees who finally arrive on the stage and who are able to continue their career in a ballet company for many years, but were they available the result would probably prove a shock both to teachers and the public. In the writer's experience the physical factor predominates very largely in those who fall by the wayside, and it is in the hope of minimising this wastage that this book is written. This does not mean to say, of course, that only those suitable for a professional career should learn ballet. Apart from its artistic merits, it is far too valuable in the training of posture, of disciplined and beautiful movement, mental alertness and concentration to be kept for the chosen few, but it does mean that care and discrimination should be brought to bear in the choice of those hoping to train professionally, and who in so doing are forced to give up many activities that belong to childhood and the world of school.

One final word. The purpose of this book is not to provide anatomical understanding of the body but rather to direct the observer's eye to those points, good and bad, which may be seen amongst any group of children attending auditions. The author is taking it for granted that the reader already possesses the rudiments of anatomy as set forth in her previous book, *Anatomy and Ballet*, and on the whole the dancer's language is used rather than the anatomist's in describing the different parts of the body and such deviations from the perfect as may affect the student in the course of training.

PART I

BALLET AND PHYSIQUE

THE PROPORTIONS OF THE BODY

IT is well recognised that a ballet dancer must possess a physique that can be trained to the finest degree of co-ordination, combined with complete flexibility, endurance, and great strength from head to toes. In spite of this all-important fact, and perhaps unfortunately, a student may train till well on into her teens before being defeated by some physical characteristic which undoubtedly existed at ten years old but was overlooked or ignored at that time. For the purpose of this book therefore we will take as our candidate a child of ten or thereabouts, and conduct a physical examination with a view to deciding upon her fitness to train for a professional career. But first we will decide upon what would be the ideal. For this, one of the most important requirements will be found to be the proportions of the body. Apart from aesthetic considerations, which are of course of the utmost importance, the body which is well proportioned will weather the stresses and strains of the exacting work required of it with greater ease than one in which there is some disparity in the relative length for instance, of limbs to torso, of width to length of the body, or of the relative size of shoulders to hips and so on. Unlike the musician, the ballet dancer cannot tune her instrument by lengthening or shortening the strings, increasing or decreasing the tension until the exact pitch is achieved. Her body is her instrument, infinitely complicated and her servant only after many years of desperately hard training. At best it becomes an instrument of great beauty, but it will fall short of this if it is endowed with that extra inch here or too short a length there to fall into that perfection of line and form that the art demands. Moreover, in the well-formed, well-proportioned physique there is less likelihood of muscles thickening in unwanted places, and less proneness to the minor and sometimes major mishaps caused by the effort to overcome obstacles which are inherent in the build of the body.

First and foremost therefore our ideal candidate would possess a body in which there shows a balance between the upper and lower

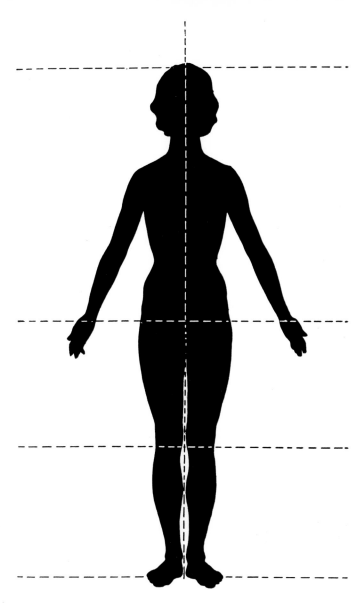

FIGURE I. THE PROPORTIONS OF THE BODY

halves of the body. A good guide for the best proportions may be
taken from ancient Greece in which the length from the crown of the
head to the pubic arch or fork is equal to that from the fork to the
ground. Following the same pattern, the length from the fork to
the lower border of the knee cap should be equal to that from the
lower border of the knee cap to the ground. (figure 1.)

According to the classical tradition, the shoulders of the man are broader than the hips, in the woman they are somewhat narrower. Here we diverge somewhat, for it has been found by experience that the ideal ballet figure is the better for some slight extra width across the shoulders, whether male or female.

The neck line is important, rather more on aesthetic grounds than from the anatomical point of view. To conform to our ideal it should not be too square, and above all not too short; the head should not be disproportionately large nor too small. (figure 2.)

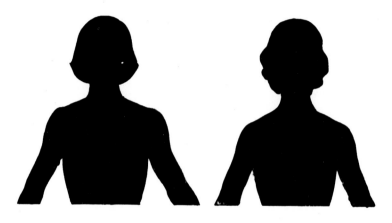

FIGURE 2. NOTE THE MORE PLEASING NECK LINE OF THE FIGURE
ON THE RIGHT

Limbs come next for our judgement as to perfection. Pretty arms and hands are naturally an asset; extra arm length or lack of it is not of any serious consequence, but for the lower limbs the standard of beauty will be high. The ideal leg will of course be straight and shapely, showing little or no muscular development when standing, with a smooth line from the back view, and knees which do not protrude too much from the front. There will be a straight line down the centre of the thigh, through the centre of the knee, down the front of the leg to about the middle of the foot. The foot will be flexible, showing at least a potential arch, with toes of medium length only and preferably with the first two or three approximating to the same length.

Finally our perfect candidate will have an upright easy carriage and well-poised head.

Now, envisaging the unlikely event of this perfect candidate appearing at an audition, how can the examiner be certain that growth and maturity will not change the physique? The answer is of course that she cannot, but certain characteristics are established by ten years old in the vast majority of cases. For instance observation has shown that the child in whom upper and lower half is beautifully balanced according to our criterion at ten will be so by twenty; the child who has a short trunk and long legs at ten will be the same at twenty, the long back will still be long in proportion to the legs at any age; and moreover, the perfectly proportioned structure will remain so whether the child grows tall, thin, heavy, petite or junoesque. The relation of one part of the body to the other does not alter whatever may happen in general terms during subsequent growth.

This does not by any means imply that within these proportions there is only one type of acceptable physique. A tall thin child may conform equally with the short plump one and the one is as suitable for training as the other. Indeed, although the present vogue seems to be entirely in favour of the sylph, we may hope that the future choreographer will re-discover the warmth and quality of movement that can be the contribution of the rounder, plumper type of dancer that we have known in the past.

By and large then we may take it that growth will not alter the proportions of the body. More difficult to forecast is the question of weight, contour and above all height. One is sometimes presented with a perfectly made but diminutive child, or one well above average height for her age. What is going to happen in the next few years? Help on this point may be sought from scientific work that is going on in America and also at the Institute of Child Health in London, where with the help of X-ray films showing the stage of the development of the bones, it is possible for the expert in this field of study to determine whether a child is merely late in growing, has arrived at what for him is his own normal stature, or is in advance of his age; and with this data to give a valuable forecast as to the ultimate height which he is likely to attain. Such assistance can be invaluable.

Weight and girth are always somewhat unpredictable, but with the experience of watching many children over a period of years, one begins to have a reasonable if not infallible picture as to how they will develop. It is not often that a really acceptable ten-year old becomes completely unsuitable physically, although with any type of child there may be an alarming phase in the early teens, from which the student of eighteen emerges, having regained in a mature form her early satisfactory outlines.

To anyone who is in the unenviable position of making the final decision as to a candidate's entry into the ballet school of her choice, the appearance of the undeniably suitable structure is a welcome if somewhat rare event, but it is obvious that if the choice were limited to the perfect there would be few ballet companies in the country, and incidentally some of our finest dancers would have been lost to the public. Now therefore whilst bearing in mind the ideal build we will consider in the next chapter some types of physique which fall short of this, deciding where and for what reason it is wise or necessary to discourage the applicant, and where defects may be overlooked or even corrected.

VARIATIONS IN PROPORTIONS

There can be little question that the purely classical dancer has the gift of a beautifully proportioned body. Apart from her technique and artistry, it is that which gives such aesthetic pleasure to the audience. Fortunately there are other rôles in the field of character and *demi-caractère* dancing where those who are not so perfectly endowed can shine with equal brilliance. We will now consider the pros and cons of the two types most usually seen which cannot be considered as perfect from the classical point of view, but yet can be accepted for training. These fall roughly into two categories,

(a) Long back with correspondingly short legs.
(b) Short back with correspondingly long legs.

Both have certain difficulties from the structural point of view.

The spine, it will be remembered, is composed of a series of small bones, known as vertebrae, separated by cushions of relatively soft material called the intervertebral discs. The vertebrae are connected to each other by tough fibrous bands called ligaments. The vertebrae vary according to the region of the spine in which they occur, those in the neck being small and thin, those in the chest region somewhat larger and those in the lower back, adapted for carrying the weight of the trunk, are altogether heavier and more solid in shape. (figures 3 and 4.)

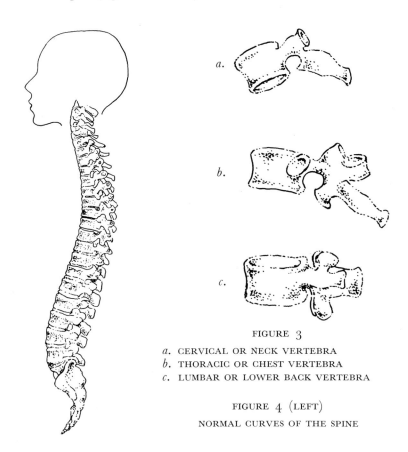

FIGURE 3

a. CERVICAL OR NECK VERTEBRA
b. THORACIC OR CHEST VERTEBRA
c. LUMBAR OR LOWER BACK VERTEBRA

FIGURE 4 (LEFT)

NORMAL CURVES OF THE SPINE

It is obvious that the longer the back, the greater the weight that has to be borne and it will be found therefore that in the long-backed type of physique (figure 6), the lower vertebrae are big, and as a safeguard the ligaments and muscles joining them will be tight and strong, limiting the movement in order to secure strength. The actual difference in flexibility may be slight considered from the standpoint of everyday life, but it is sufficient to become a real obstacle in the training of the dancer. Such backs are not designed for the extreme flexibility that is required for the perfect *arabesque* or *attitude* for example, and in trying to cultivate it there is undue strain on muscles and ligaments, and pressure on the discs in the lumbar region. Not a few of the complaints of low back pain have come to the notice of the author in students of this type. Alternatively one sees such dancers avoiding the difficulty by twisting the hips in movement such as *grands battements derrière* and destroying the line of the arabesque by taking it vitually *à la seconde*. (figure 5.)

FIGURE 5

BY TWISTING THE HIPS THE LINE OF THE ARABESQUE IS DESTROYED

(*From a drawing by Patrick Furse*)

It is fortunate that a very marked figure of this type is seen more often in boys than in girls, where it is more manageable. The prospect for either is character dancing rather than classical and the student would be well advised to accept certain limitations in movement without straining after the impossible.

The short torso may be combined with narrow hips, in which case one can state categorically that there will never be sufficient strength in back and hips to meet the demands of more than elementary work, and this is one type of physique that the examiner may reject without too much indecision. (figure 7.) Nobody knows better than the ballet dancer how much strength is required in the hip muscles to perform even the simplest *adage*. When the back is short the legs are of course long in proportion, and correspondingly more effort is therefore needed to lift them and hold them in various balletic positions. Narrow, small hips are badly equipped for this purpose especially as at the same time there is invariably lacking a natural turn-out. One finds very little improvement as regards strength and turn-out in the short-torsoed narrow-hipped child even after two or three years of training.

On the other hand one also sees a type with short back but full hips (figure 8.) Here the question becomes nearer the aesthetic, since there is likely to be strength enough but a lack of beauty in

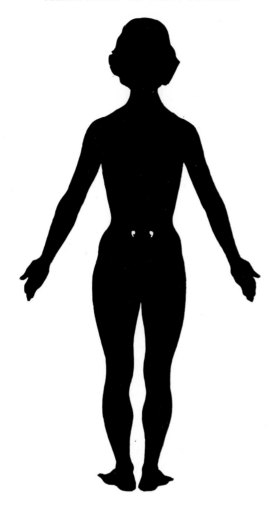

FIGURE 6
THE LONG-BACKED TYPE OF PHYSIQUE

line, due to heavy hips and thighs in later growth. In addition, in this type the back is usually very flexible and tends to sink in the mid-region too readily in movements *derrière*, the ribs protruding and creating an ugly prominence in front. This may already be notice-able at ten years old, so that if such a child is accepted, care will be needed to ensure that the condition does not increase and in so doing weaken the spine. It is definitely a case for careful consider-ation and the weighing in the balance of talent *versus* physique.

C

FIGURE 7. SHORT TORSO
WITH NARROW HIPS

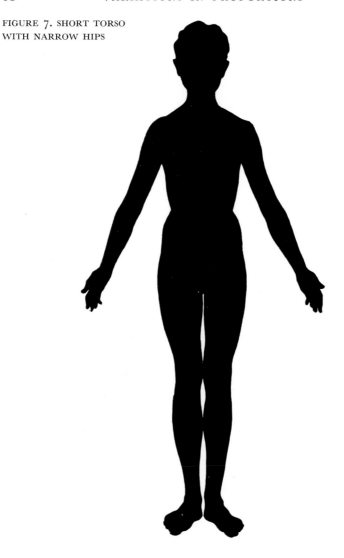

Between these two major types there will naturally be many others. The proportions in length may be satisfactory, in girth less determinate. It is difficult at this early age to foresee what will happen in the round, as it were, but fat is less of an enemy to the potential trainee than over-developed muscles. Fat will absorb and is not a reliable indication of future type. Many plump ten-year-olds grow tall and lanky in their teens and vice versa. The muscular child, however, will always be muscular, of that one may be assured. If the examiner is concentrating on girls of the svelte, stream-lined

FIGURE 8. SHORT TORSO
WITH FULL HIPS

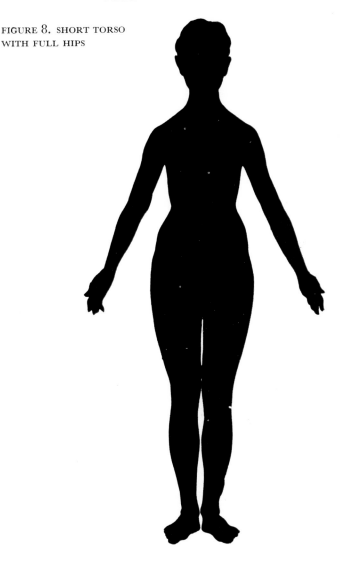

type of the present vogue, she will reject the candidate who at ten
already shows athletic bulges of muscles in thighs and legs, for they
will be equally noticeable at any age, whatever her proportions. In
boys it is naturally of less importance, but it should be understood
that bulk of muscles is not synonymous with strength. It is elasticity
which gives the muscles both endurance and strength and renders
them less prone to accidents. Many ballerinas have steel-like
strength in muscles which are practically invisible.

In our ideal candidate, the measurement from hip to knee was approximately the same as from knee to the ground. When the thigh is short from hip to knee it is most often combined with the long back and the disadvantages therefore are concerned with those referred to in that connection. Moreover, the chances are that being short, growth will take place in girth as well as length, resulting in heavy bulky thighs and correspondingly big hips. It becomes an aesthetic rather than anatomical question and as has already been mentioned, occurs more often in boys than girls.

The short lower leg is seen more often in girls but this is not a serious matter from the point of view of technique. Indeed, it is often found amongst those with good elevation, and of course is less noticeable when the dancer is on *pointe*. Only an unusual degree of shortening need be considered seriously and then the legs will in any case be muscular and ugly.

The *straightness* of the legs is of great importance, and some judgement is required in deciding how far deviations may be over-looked. The three most common variations in the alignment are:

> Knock-knees
> Bow legs
> "Sway-back" or over-extended knees.

Before discussing these, it may help to revise very briefly the anatomical formation of the lower limbs.

The lower half of the body consists of the pelvic girdle, a series of six bones joined to each other and to the sacrum behind to form a basin-like cavity. This cavity is wider and shallower in the female than in the male. (figures 9 a & b.) On the outer side, the femur (thigh) with its rounded head fits into a cup-shaped socket and by virtue of the shape of the pelvis slopes inward, expanding at the lower end into two bony masses (condyles) to form part of the knee joint. The shaft of this bone is not straight, but curves forward. The lower leg consists of two bones (tibia and fibula) the larger of which (tibia) forms the knee joint with the femur. A complicated system of ligaments and muscles connects these bones, allowing the joint to move in the manner of a hinge, and in the last moment of tightening, with a very small rotation of the tibia on the femur. (figure 10.)

FIGURE 9   FIGURE 10

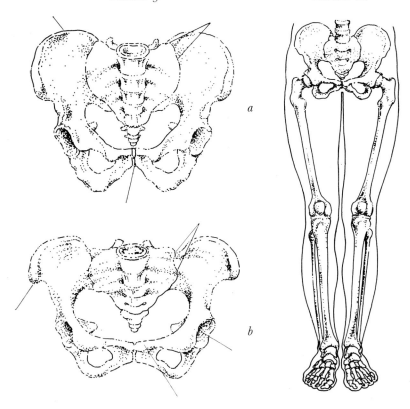

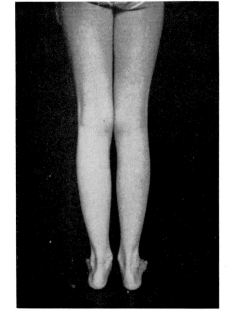

FIGURE 9. THE PELVIC GIRDLE;
a, MALE; *b*, FEMALE

FIGURE 10. THE BONES OF
THE LEGS

FIGURE 11

A greater degree of knock
knee than is here shown is
likely to be a severe handicap
in the slim type of structure.
Note also the "rolling" right
foot, often found in con-
junction with knock knees.

KNOCK-KNEES

From this brief resumé it will be clear that the shape of the pelvis and position of the thigh is an important factor in determining the straightness of the legs as a whole. If the slope inwards is exaggerated, either because of the width of the pelvis, or as sometimes happens, an unusually small angle at the upper end of the femur, there will result the condition we recognise as knock-knees.

A small degree of this may be considered normal in girls—due as already pointed out, to the naturally wider pelvis and consequent greater slope inwards of the thigh. The simplest test can be made, back view for choice, by standing the child with feet only very slightly turned out, knees just touching. There should normally then be not more than 1-in. between the heels (allowing that chubby ten-year-old may still have a certain amount of fat between the thighs which would prevent the knees closing completely). It is important that this test should be made with *very* little turn-out as otherwise the inner condyles of the femur—which may be large at this age and smaller in proportion later on—will prevent the heels from coming together and give a false impression as to the degree of knock-knee existing.

How much greater mal-alignment may be permitted is a matter for balancing up the general physique against this particular disadvantage. The compact sturdy type can overcome a degree of knock-knee up to 2in. but in no case is more than this desirable. In a thin tall child with poor musculature there is likely to be some slackness of the knee joint indicating weakness and the possibility of trouble later on.

Moreover, there will be difficulty in acquiring speed, elevation and strong *pointe* work since the thrust from the floor when knock-knees are present is taken, not in a straight line from foot to hip, but in one weakened by an angle at the knee joint and imposing a strain both on foot and knee. Markedly knock-knees with or without laxness in the joint may subsequently account for many of the ligamentous strains, slipped cartilages or various inflammations within the knee joint which are met with from time to time, and even for those strains of the foot, often difficult to locate accurately, which seem to arise for no obvious reason. Figure 11 shows the limit desirable in this formation.

A word of warning must here be given against the hope that a child of ten will outgrow knock-knees. A very young child may do so for the reason that the condition is due to unequal development of the two condyles of the femur, the inner having grown faster than the outer; a child, boy or girl, then appears startlingly knock-kneed at three and recovers completely by five years old, but the type that is met with at ten does not belong to this category.

BOW-LEGS

There are two main types of bow legs. One is that in which the femur is normal but the tibia curves outward. An occasional boy may come up for audition with this formation but one does not find it amongst girls. Probably they have already been discouraged from learning ballet by a discriminating parent or teacher. The second type is met with in both sexes, though the degree is more marked in boys. In this the bowing includes the thighs so that when the feet are touching there is a space between the knees. This is not strictly a bowing of the legs. The space between the knees occurs by virtue of the fact that the curve of the femur instead of being situated on the front of the thigh has deviated somewhat to the outer side, thus changing the position of the condyles, which then face slightly inward instead of to the front, so causing the space between the knees. (figure 12.) The real drawback to this formation lies in the fact that the hip joint is always by nature in-turned and to that extent this type of bow leg interferes with perfect technical accomplishment; and of course it is ugly in girls and does not add to the charm of the male dancer. However, in the male one usually finds good elevation with some degree of bow leg, in girls it is more variable, depending on whether or no the position of the legs affects that of the feet. Again, as with knock-knees, it must not be imagined that training will correct the bowing. It can be disguised when the feet are both on the ground, close together, toes and heels touching and the whole limb rotated outward in the hips, so that momentarily the legs appear straight, but as soon as this effort is released they will return to the original position, after even twenty years of training.

"SWAY-BACK" KNEES

The last variation we are considering is the over-extended or "sway-back" knee. This may be a remnant of infantile bow-legs, with which it is often accompanied, in which the knees are pressed backward too far, leaving the ligaments at the back permanently

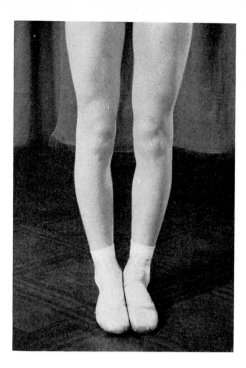

FIGURE 12

Bow-legs with inturned hips
which make difficulties for
the dancer. Note the "rolling" left foot due to this
formation of the legs.

stretched and the front of the knee too flat or almost hollow with a
bulge above. (figure 13.) One sees this more often than formerly,
which gives rise to the conjecture as to whether there may not
also be a further cause, namely that the child with slight bow legs,
or even without, has begun ballet too early, has been told to "pull
up the thighs", and has responded by pressing back the knees,
resulting in this sway-back position. Be that as it may the result
is disastrous from the point of view of training, since the 'placing'
of the body is completely upset, the weight falling on the heels and
any pulling up of the thighs increasing the trouble. Speed and elevation are affected and in a marked case of this kind it would be folly
to accept the candidate. Even a very slight degree will need the
careful adjustment of many exercises and a watchful eye from an
experienced teacher. Perhaps the last criterion in the case of a
promising child with this obstacle should be her intelligence to use
the guidance that may be given her. In figures 14 and 15 can be seen
this formation in a 12-year-old corrected in appearance by bringing
the hip forward and the weight on to the front of the foot—a very
difficult adjustment to make throughout every exercise and movement.

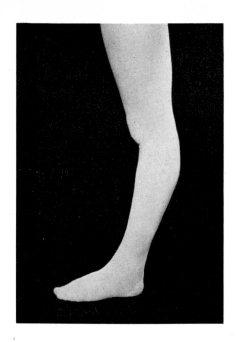

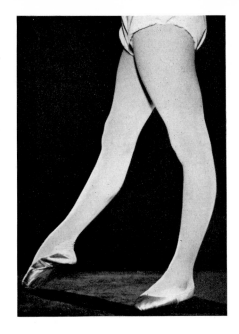

FIGURE 13

FIGURE 14

FIGURE 13. "Sway-back" knees with overdeveloped muscle above, probably the result of infantile bow-legs.

FIGURE 14. "Sway-back" knees, possibly caused by pressing back the knees instead of pulling up the thigh muscles.

FIGURE 15. Appearance improved by adjustment of weight, a continuous effort not possible to sustain throughout all movements.

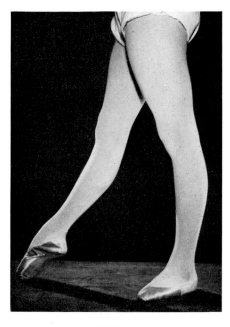

FIGURE 15

Passing now to feet, we come to the most difficult of all decisions. Feet vary as much as the hand and are of as many shapes, and it would be a prophet indeed who could declare with certainty what will be the result of the next years of training on any, however perfect, at ten years old. Height and weight are undoubtedly factors, as is also the good alignment of the legs. The less weight the feet are called upon to bear, the more they will be spared of the stresses and strains of the highly specialised use to which they are put in ballet, more especially in *pointe* work. The straighter the legs the more easily the weight will fall correctly on the strongest part of the feet. Toes of medium length forming a round pattern on the floor hold the ground more firmly than those too long and slender, and give strength to the push off in steps of elevation. A large big toe is a distinct asset. A medium arch is sufficient in our ten-year-old and there should be complete and free movement in the ankle joint allowing the foot to be turned up to form a right angle to the leg, and pointed to make a smooth line over the front of the ankle. (figure 16.)

Watching the feet with these points in mind, one may find endless variations which yet add up to a satisfactory verdict. The type that may give one to pause is the very highly arched foot which leaves no room for further development. No part of the body should at this early age represent the end product of training, for it will then not be capable of gaining the necessary strength. Tempting though it may be to hail with joy an enormous arch, in actual experience it will be found that it is a handicap, and is particularly prone to trouble in the early teens, more especially if it is combined with a too flexible spine, weak musculature and particularly, with long thin toes. It is far better to look for the foot which is perhaps a little tight but shows the beginning of an arch, providing always that the movement in the ankle joint is free. Should that not be so, there is little likelihood of an arch developing, as the limitation will be due to the bony formation of the end of the tibia and the bones of the back part of the foot. From time to time one finds students of sixteen years or so complaining of foot pain of one kind or another due to trying by force to loosen the foot sufficiently to get well up on *pointe*. The trouble lies not in the foot itself but in the ankle joint in which some slight variation in the shape of the bones prevents any further movement. There is a limit to the amount the

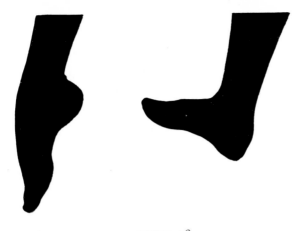

FIGURE 16

bones concerned, the calcaneum and talus, will roll over each other and nothing will change it. (See figure 18E.) In considering a ten-year-old, however, a test should be made to decide whether the limitation is apparent or real. It may be that the child has never fully used the joint and it will then be found that on the half point a good arch appears with a smooth line above it over the ankle joint. In the case of a really tight ankle joint, a good half point cannot be taken.

Alternatively. a short achilles tendon may prevent the upward movement of the ankle without interfering with the arch of the foot. A true shortening is not common, but if it does exist it brings with it technical problems in getting the heels down in *pliés, fondus* and springs, with consequent wear and tear on the feet and thickening of the calf muscles. An apparent shortening will yield to correct effort, but if it is structural it is a definite handicap.

Next comes the vexed question of the "rolling" foot. These fall into two categories, the "flat" or "valgus" foot of the clinic, which is stiff and has no arch, and the flexible foot in which the arch falls when standing still, but appears at once on movement. A child of ten who has learnt ballet previously may come under this heading. It need not cause her rejection, as if she has not already been taught to hold the foot in the correct position in standing she can, in the year or two before she begins *pointe* work, learn how to do so and gain the strength in the foot and leg muscles to hold the correction.

The clinical flat foot, however, will never be a "dancer's" foot and is not suitable for a ballet career.

There now remains the question as to what type of foot will escape the occupational hazard of the ballet dancer, the enlarged big toe joint which is deflected inwards, technically known as *hallux valgus*. Probably if one could compare the incidence of this trouble in dancers with that of any body of people using their feet as mercilessly, we should find that there was not much to choose between the two, and indeed there are many dancers whose feet remain perfect after a long career; but there are also those who show signs of enlargement of the joint at an early age. When the condition arises after the foot is strong and well trained, it seems to give little or no trouble, but if an audition candidate should present herself with a marked degree of *hallux valgus* at ten years old—and it does happen —it is asking too much to hope that she will survive the training without disability. She may continue for a year or two, but with the introduction of *pointe* work, her career is more than likely to come to an end. Two very different types of foot are particularly prone to this trouble, the foot that has a high arch and long thin toes, and surprisingly, the broad male foot. The long thin foot combined with knock-knees is also vulnerable, whereas a foot which has a short vamp and medium arch, often with the first three toes almost the same length is often found to be well-nigh indestructible. It is, however, impossible to give more than a few suggestions of this kind, for too little research has as yet been made on the problem, even amongst the general population, to form a basis for any hard and fast rules. It is as well to remember too that early signs of this condition may be caused, not by ballet, but by unsuitable footwear. The outgrown shoe and short socks can do as much to produce it as a dancing class. If the signs are very slight and the foot good, strong and flexible, with medium arch and short toes, the risk may be taken and safeguards taken against any progression of the trouble by the utmost care in correct execution of all movements, and above all the right footwear both in class and street.

A word of caution may be given before leaving this subject against mistaking a large joint for one which is enlarged. Bones grow by virtue of the pull of the muscle tendons inserted into them and since this pull is stronger than normal in ballet one often finds the big toe joint appears large. Unless there is also some redness or swelling it may be a perfectly normal joint. The deflection of the toe inwards

is the important factor to consider, combined with close questioning
as to the presence of pain, however slight, in movement.

EXAMPLES OF FEET

The illustrations which follow show the feet of six student
dancers, between 17–19 years of age, none of whom have had
any foot trouble during their training, averaging 9 years, with
the exception of E, who for a short time was off work with pain
around the ankle joint. This was probably due to the inherent
tightness of the joint and the effort to loosen it as *pointe* work
increased. Other than this, the illustrations demonstrate the difficulty of making categorical statements as to which type of foot will
withstand the training and what kind of execution can be expected
of it. For instance, in general a very high arch does not make for
good elevation, yet both B and F have exceptionally high springs;
but as would be expected, they are only slowly getting that quick
footwork for which strong muscles in the sole of the foot are necessary
and which are rarely found combined with a high arch. C on the
other hand conforms to type in having little elevation and A in
lacking speed. Both D and E are strong in action but E, with
little arch and tight ankle joint which will not loosen further is
a *demi-caractère* dancer in the making and wisely accepts the
fact.

It will be seen that both A and D have a slight degree of *hallux
valgus*. This began only in their late teens, by which time the foot
is fully grown and well trained, when some deviation in the joint
seems then to give no trouble.

The only factors which appear to be common to all six are the
large big toe, broad front and the rounded pattern which the toes
make on the floor. In none of them is there a sharp decrease in the
length of the toes from 1st to 5th and this may well be of greater
importance in the wearing quality of the foot than has yet been
recognised.

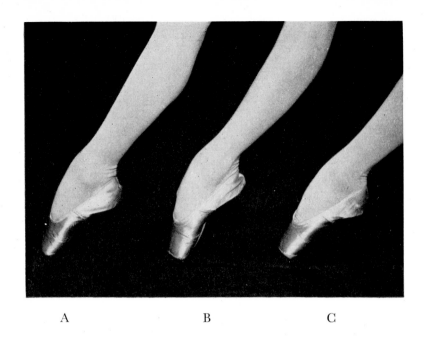

A   B   C

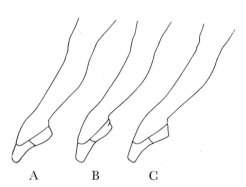

A B C

FIGURE I7. A, B AND C. THE FEET OF THREE STUDENT DANCERS
(SEE NOTE ON PAGE 29)

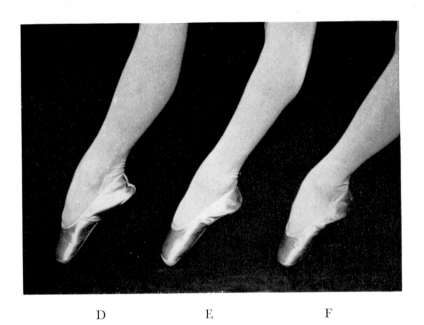

D   E   F

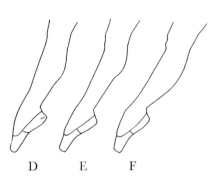

D   E   F

FIGURE 18. D, E AND F. THE FEET OF THREE OTHER STUDENT DANCERS
(SEE NOTE ON PAGE 29)

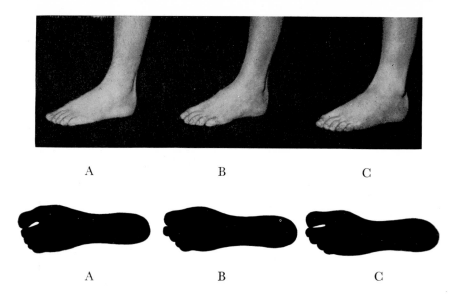

A   B   C

A   B   C

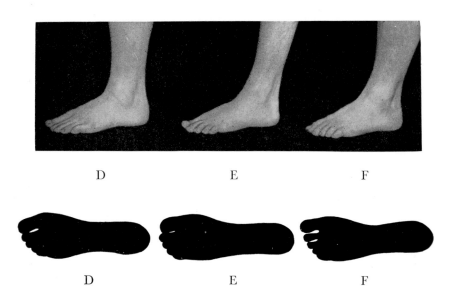

D   E   F

D   E   F

FIGURES 19 AND 20: FEET

(SEE NOTE ON PAGE 29 AND FIGURES 17 AND 18)

N.B.—The silhouette drawings, being made from the photographs above, are designed to show the shape of the forefoot and toes. The arch therefore is not indicated, as would be the case in footprints.

POSTURE

There is still a last question, the posture of the child. Ideally there should be perfect symmetry of both sides of the body and a good upright stance. Many children, however, have some small degree of asymmetry of the body and would not satisfy this test. One shoulder will appear a little higher than the other, the line of the torso to the waist will not be the same on the one side as the other and the points of the ears and shoulder blades are not level. (figure 21.) There may be some structural reason for this, possibly one leg a fraction longer than the other, or there may be some irregularity in the vertebrae of the spine such as to produce a lateral curvature. The latter can be checked by asking the child to bend downward as far as possible, head tucked in towards the knees. In this position there should be no sign of a bulge of the ribs on the one side nor any flattening on the other; one shoulder blade should not appear more prominent than the other and there should be no sign of the muscles in the lower back appearing fuller on one side than the other. If the contour of the back, viewed at eye level, not looking downwards from above, appears identical on either side it is safe to say that the asymmetry which is seen in the standing position does not involve the spine to any extent that would interfere with the training, providing —and this is an important reservation—that movements of the hips are equally free on both sides, such tests as *grands battements*, *développés*, *arabesques* forming a useful criterion. It would be unwise to accept a candidate if there is any doubt whatever on the result of this test without a further orthopaedic opinion, for anything abnormal in the structure of the spine must handicap the dancer, if not make training undesirable.

The back which shows some asymmetry with no corresponding spinal abnormality to account for it is very common and is considered by modern orthopaedic surgeons to be a failure of the muscles on either side of the spine which are responsible for the maintenance of posture to receive and respond equally to the nerve impulses connecting the brain to the muscles, a failure which may be due to fatigue, too rapid growth or even emotional instability. Certainly one finds this condition in children with excitab e and sensitive temperaments and very often with an insecure background. In such there is a steady improvement as training proceeds and the whole poise of the body is stabilised. By the third year of training

E

there will be nothing left to see—but not necessarily before that time.

If the asymmetry is due to some slight difference in the length of the legs, it will not disappear, but the body adapts and the mature dancer is able to manage the small problems it creates. They are not of sufficient consequence to cause the rejection of a talented child with an otherwise suitable physique, but there may be a limit to final brilliant accomplishment with this handicap.

There are many other formations of the back which must be considered, the spine which has a longer than normal curve back-ward in the mid-region leaving a short lumbar hollow and sharp angle as it meets the sacrum, a difficult back to alter, since "pulling the tail under" does not plane out the hollow, but only increases the rounding above; the too flat back with a sharp angle at the base and often combined with large hips and stiffness of movement in the lower back, and one in which pulling the tail under is apt to produce a curve backward in the lumbar region. This last irregularity, a spine which shows a curve backward in the lumbar region in place of the normal hollow, was at one time a rarity. Now one finds it too often and the question comes to mind as to whether it is the result of too much interference with posture in young children. The injunction often heard, "pull the tail under," may be a

FIGURE 21

The appearance of an asymmetrical spine of the type which often has no structural basis. Note uneven level of ears and shoulder line and apparent displacement of the body to the left.

FIGURE 22. LUMBAR
CURVE REVERSED (COM-
PARE FIGURE 4)

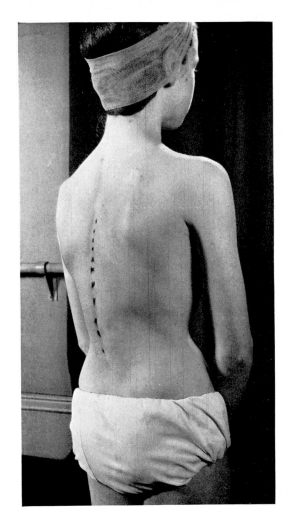

necessary correction for a very hollow backed child, but may suc-
ceed in reversing the hollow in a flexible child not in need of such a
correction. The point is worth considering, for the result is a weak
back which tires quickly even in everyday life. We have no record
as yet as to what will happen to such in ten or fifteen years' time,
but we would hazard a guess that they will feature amongst the
slipped discs and sacro-iliac strains when the full work of a stage
career overtakes them. Figure 22 shows such a back at 12 years old.
In a tunic the posture appears good. Lesser degrees are also found,
often with some sinking in between the shoulders, but still passing
as good stance when clothed.

A few candidates at auditions appear with the more easily
recognised types of bad posture—round shoulders, poking head, etc.

On the whole one can look to their training to correct this. A test easily made is to ascertain whether or no lengthening the spine improves the condition, the child standing in third position, and making herself as tall as possible. Gentle pressure downwards on the top of the head, to increase the effort of lengthening by pushing upwards, may be a useful expedient and the result will show whether the spine is adjustable and the stance likely to improve.

Shoulder blades in a thin child which stick out and are too prominent at this age may be ignored. They will flatten as time goes on and be less noticeable as they get a greater covering of flesh in the teens: or possibly, in a permanently thin type of physique, they will always be prominent, but do not affect the stance.

FLEXIBILITY

Presumably the dancing audition has satisfied the examiner that the candidate is potentially sufficiently flexible throughout for her age. Apparent stiffness may be tue to tension or wrong effort—this is often noticeable in *barre* exercises where the child is contracting the back muscles instead of lengthening them and so appears stiff in the hip and lower back. (Tension, be it noted, that may be in the over-anxious teacher and reproduced in the pupil.) On the other hand as we have already said, in the long-backed, the narrow-hipped, the bow-legged, tightness in the hip is structural and not likely to be completely overcome. The knobbly knee, apparently slightly bent in standing, if not due to short hamstring muscles, may be habit only and a smooth line can be secured by effort; and so with the ankle joint which has not been fully used. These points and others can be tested by the examiner when in doubt as to the flexibility of any child.

There can never be a last word on the question of the suitability of a gifted little ten-year-old for professional training, there will always be the urge to hope, and to take a chance, but it is desirable that the parents should know of any doubts in the mind of the examiner, and in the border-line case to make the final decision. For the child who has definitely unsuitable feet or legs, or is definitely wrong in structure for ballet, it is far kinder to be uncompromising in rejection. For the one parent who will say "nobody has ever complained about my child before" there will be twenty who will be genuinely grateful for the advice to turn the child's interests in other directions whilst there is time, disappointing though it may be; and it is not unknown for the child to have her or his own plans. "If I can't be a dancer, I want to be a veterinary surgeon—or a nurse—or a sailor—". These incongruous alternatives have all been presented to the author at different times and one suspects in such cases that it is parental pressure that has been brought to bear upon the choice of ballet for the candidate's career rather than the ardour which is the hall mark of the 10-year old devotee.

THE FOLLOWING QUESTIONNAIRE IS SUGGESTED FOR ALL CANDI-
DATES FOR AUDITION AS AN ADDITION TO THE NORMAL MEDICAL
CERTIFICATE:

1. Are the proportions of the body, general build and flexibility satisfactory?

2. Has there been any previous illness affecting the general health?

3. Is there any residual trouble in any joint, especially the knee due to former illness or injury?

4. Is the spine straight? If not, is the asymmetry due to
    (a) Unequal length of the legs?
    (b) Any rotation of the pelvis?
    (c) Lateral curvature?
        (i) Structural?*
        (ii) Postural?

5. Is there any trace, however small, of anything unusual in the lumbar spine, e.g. convexity instead of concavity when the child is standing upright?†

6. Are the legs straight? If not
    (a) Is there a marked degree of knock knee, i.e. more than $2\frac{1}{2}$-in. between the heels when viewed from behind, knees touching and feet pointing forward?
    (b) Bow-leg when viewed from the front, heels and toes touching?
    (c) Do the knees curve backward very markedly?*

7. Is the ankle joint mobile, i.e. foot making a right angle with the leg when turned up and smooth line with the leg when pointed down?

8. Does the whole length of the inner border of the foot rest on the ground in standing with heels and toes about 3-in. apart, feet pointing forward? Is there no sign of an arch on half *pointe* or *degagé* positions?*

9. Is there a definite and marked degree of *hallus valgus*?*

An orthopaedic surgeon's opinion may be needed to verify some of these points. Those marked * are definitely adverse signs, that marked † is at present unproven.

For children coming from a long distance, a preliminary set of photographs might save an expensive and disappointing journey. A good deal could be learned of the general make-up, the straightness or otherwise of the legs, and the type of foot from:

(a) Front view in close fitting plain bathing dress, bare feet, standing with heels together toes very slightly turned out.

(b) As (a), heels and toes touching.

(c) As (a), one foot *dégagé* in 2nd position.

(d) Back view, heels about 3-in. apart, feet looking straight forward.

DANCERS' PHYSIQUE

The following photographs have been chosen as all corresponding to the criteria already submitted, and yet as illustrating both similarity and diversity in physique. It is the diversity rather than the similarity that gives each dancer her distinctive appeal. Note for example the warm emotional quality of Baronova as opposed to the athletic strength of Maria Tallchief; Mary Ellen Moylan, petite and elegant; the sharply defined steel-like lines of Melissa Hayden; tall statuesque Beriosova, and Moira Shearer, lithe and gay; Markova, whose ethereal quality derives from her lightly built body and above all Margot Fonteyn (frontispiece) giving in *La Péri*, the effect of an oriental vase, beautifully, delicately balanced, the artistic perfection of technique and physique.

ALICIA MARKOVA AND MILORAD MISKOVITCH

Serge Lido

IRINA BARONOVA
Maurice Seymour

MARY ELLEN MOYLAN
Walter E. Owen

MARIA TALLCHIEF
Walter E. Owen

MELISSA HAYDEN

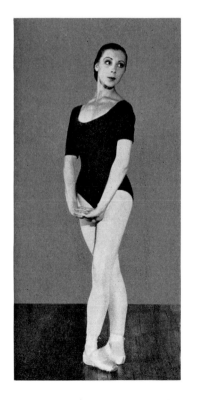

MOIRA SHEARER
Gordon Anthony

The illustrations on the page facing show:

ABOVE (LEFT) TAMARA TOUMANOVA
(*Gordon Anthony*)

ABOVE (RIGHT) JANINE CHARRAT
(*Lido*)

BELOW (LEFT) SVETLANA BERIOSOVA
(*Paul Wilson*)

BELOW (RIGHT) BRIAN SHAW
(*Baron*)

43

DAVID BLAIR
Gordon Anthony

INJURIES, PREVENTION AND CURE

GENERAL COMMENTS

WHEN we consider what is demanded of the framework of the body from the time of the first lesson at the *barre* to the appearance of the dancer on the stage, it is not surprising that from time to time there should be mishaps, and that protesting muscles, joints and ligaments should occasionally give trouble. Yet on the whole there is remarkably little that goes wrong, provided that the pupil has no structural defects, speaking from the point of view of ballet training. During the early years, up to about twelve years of age, complaints of aches and pains are normally trivial. During the teens and with the advent of *pointe* work, they are liable to need more consideration, and of course with the heavy time-table of the professional dancer, and at times the modern choreographer's sublime disregard for the limitations of the human body, injuries, as apart from strain, are more likely to occur. Nevertheless they are rare in proportion to the number of performers involved, and though it may seem, as we list the possibilities, that ballet is a dangerous career leaving in its trail a long list of casualties, in actual fact the record both for fitness and freedom from disabling mishaps in a ballet company is extremely good, and this in spite of the long hours of work and rehearsals, irregular meals and lack of fresh air.

There are a certain number of typical stresses and strains that may be found in any ballet school, or indeed in classes for amateurs who often go beyond merely elementary work. Some of these undoubtedly would not be heard of were every pupil perfectly constructed for ballet training, or even if those with special and similar difficulties could be taught together. We have already referred to the danger of such general injunctions as "pull up the thighs" and "tuck in the tail" which may be necessary for the majority but unwise for such types of backs as figures 26 and knees as seen in figures 13 and 14. Short of this idealistic conception of the classroom, however, some precautions can be taken if the teacher is aware of the make-up of each pupil. This entails that she should see them at intervals in bare feet and at the most a bathing slip only. Children are intelligent little creatures about their own bodies and can be shown quite young how to work with special relation to their own physical problems. For example, had the children in figures 13 and 14 been told to avoid pulling up the thighs too strongly at eight years old it is certain that there would have been a much lesser degree, if any, of "sway-back" in the knees at eighteen and twelve respectively, and so with the twelve-year-old back in illustration 22. Apart from these manifest cases, however, there are the small aches and pains which are often related to some physical particularity and it may be possible to find the link, and so deal with both prevention and cure.

Before going into further details of such, it must be made clear that the object in discussing them is not in any way to discourage the seeking of medical advice. Indeed, in certain cases it is imperative to do so; but the majority are transient and trivial, and the average medical practitioner, who cannot be expected to understand the niceties of ballet technique, can usually do no more than prescribe rest, or dismiss them as unimportant; as indeed they are, but may yet render the dancer unable to work in class. Our object here is merely to help the teacher to discriminate between those small aches which follow a very definite pattern and the more serious pains which should be referred for medical diagnosis. Nor is the intention to ignore the various forms of treatment that may sometimes be neces-sary—physiotherapy, manipulation, injection and so on—but rather to help on such treatment and prevent any recurrence of the trouble by eliminating any cause for which errors in technique in the class-room may be responsible.

THE FEET

As might be expected feet figure more largely amongst complaints in the ballet class than anything else, knees running a close second. Amongst the younger children it is as well to make sure that the ache or pain is the result of exercise in the class-room. The author remem-bers a small boy who came to her complaining of pain over his instep up the front of the leg, and on top of his knee, who remembered on being questioned that he had gone for a walk on Sunday, climbed a tree and fallen in the descent! The un-typical position of the site of the pain would arouse the suspicion of anyone familiar with the pattern of ballet strains. When, however, a child complains of pain along the inner border of the foot when standing at the *barre* this, one concludes, belongs to ballet. It will most likely be found that it is due to the effort of correcting a "roll". It is not important unless it persists. If after a day or two it has not disappeared, it is better to take the child off work for a few days. Many children correct rolling feet with no resulting discomfort, but in the exception persistent pain indicates that the ligaments of the foot are feeling the strain of adjusting to the new position, and ligaments in the foot are quicker to react and slower to recover from strain than are muscles. This will often be so in the highly arched foot where the muscles are not sufficiently strong and undue work falls upon the ligaments in standing. In parenthesis it may be pointed out that it is perhaps more important that flexible highly arched feet should be trained from the very beginning to hold the correct position on the floor, ball of big toe, ball of little toe and heel, than any other type, since it is one way of strengthening the muscles of the sole of the foot which have such an important part to play in maintaining the arch, and which tend to be weak in the foot which is beautiful to look at but difficult to train. If in such, during the first few years persistent "rolling" is left unchecked, we have the soft mobile foot that gives way on *pointe*, and has no push off in elevation.

Apart from the pain along the inner side of the foot, various small aches may be found in young children for which a couple of days' rest from class is usually all that is needed. Simple home remedies need not be neglected, e.g. bathing in hot water, in which a good handful of Epsom salts has been dissolved is a simple and effective relief for many foot troubles. It can also be useful for older students, amongst whom from time to time more definite pains arise. It is not always possible to locate exactly the site of a strain in a structure so bound together by ligaments as is the foot. As work becomes more advanced there are more possibilities of pressure here or a pull there, and if such arise the most helpful procedure is to find the exact position or exercise that produces it. Eliminating this for a few days is often all that is required, and perhaps working in a light bandage when including it again in class. The elastic net type of bandage is more suitable than crêpe for this purpose, giving greater support, without bulk or undue restriction of movement. Should the pain be persistent, then strapping with adhesive strapping is more efficacious, put on by an expert, from whom also advice should be sought as to the length of time to wear it.

Strains of ligaments in the foot are felt mostly on the supporting foot, i.e. in weight bearing, and in springs, less so in holding *en l'air* or in such movements as *battements frappés*, *battements tendus* and so on. There are one or two muscles which may also be the source of trouble, but the pain will then be felt on movement rather than in standing and especially when on *pointe*. The usual place that the dancer will point to is just behind the inner ankle. (figure 23.) It occurs most often in the highly arched foot with loose ankle joint and it is fairly safe to say that it is produced by some degree, however small, of "sickling out" either on *pointe* or in other exercises or positions. It is especially necessary to deal with the cause, which harks back to faulty technique, for this strain may become a tiresome and recurring inflammation in the tendon of the muscle concerned, the Tibealis Posterior muscle as it is called. Having come down the outer side of the leg, its tendon winds round the inner ankle, spreading out into smaller tendons under the foot. Its action is to point the foot and to turn up the inner border. The stretch put upon the main tendon then is obvious if the foot is sickled out, more especially when weight bearing. Any inflammation in a tendon should be the signal for rest, and in this particular case, taken at once it will clear up in a week. If the pain is at all severe it should be seen by a doctor who will no doubt strap the foot in the exact position which speeds up recovery.

The fact that this particular strain is practically confined to the more delicate type of foot reminds us that strength and flexibility rarely go hand in hand, and it is important to work for the building up of strength in the one type and flexibility in the other. Nothing is more important to the over-mobile foot than the correct use of the resistance of the floor. It is too easy for its owner to neglect this, showing the end result of e.g. a *battement tendu* without the strong slide of the foot on the floor before arching the foot, and in steps of elevation—*assemblés*, etc.—the same tendency. It is in part at least the reason for the better elevation in the dancer who has had to work to produce a good arch than in the one who is by nature so endowed.

There is one other tendon which can give trouble, the Achilles tendon which joins the calf muscles to the heel. Pain in this should always be dealt with at once. It can occur in both boys and girls, usually not before twelve years old, but occasionally earlier in boys. The complaint is either a pain above the heel in *pliés* and *fondus* or when pointing the foot; and at a later stage on turning the foot upward. It may be caused by lack of a good *demi-plié* especially

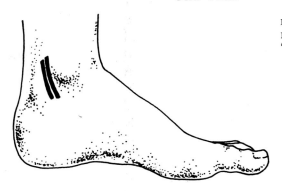

FIGURE 23. SITE OF PAIN
LIKELY TO BE CAUSED BY
"SICKLING OUT".

with a stiff type of foot, or if there exists a short Achilles tendon. Whatever the cause, all work should be stopped at once, and as a precaution it is wise to have the limb strapped for a week to ten days and for work to be resumed for a day or two before the strapping is removed. A week is the minimum rest for this condition and there should be no remnant of pain when beginning again. Nor should a full class be attempted, *relevés*, springs and of course all *pointe* work omitted for at least another week. Treated thus, this inflammation subsides but regarded as unimportant it can be one of the most disabling of the dancer's strains, becoming in time a real synovitis, with creaking in the tendon and severe pain. It is worth being on the cautious side to avoid this possibility. The doctor or other expert by whom the strapping should be put on might question the necessity of binding the limb from heel to knee for such an apparently slight condition, yet in view of the special stretch to which this tendon is subjected in ballet it is wiser to take extreme precautions immediately and so to prevent the likelihood of any recurrence of the trouble.

These strains of ligaments and tendons that have been mentioned do not of course exhaust all possibilities that may occur in the classroom, but they cover the main types which are due to the nature of the work, rather than any extraneous cause. In addition there is of course the ordinary sprained ankle, ruptured fibres in the calf muscle and in the Achilles tendon. These last two are never met in younger students. They belong to the adult dancer and need immediate medical attention. The sprained ankle may occur at almost any age, but it is an injury rather than a strain. In its mild form a very few days' rest from work is all that is necessary, but should it be severe it is quite a serious injury. The most common site of damage

G

is that of the ligament on the outer side of the ankle, divided into three bands of which the front or middle one is the most likely to suffer damage, either by overstretching or the rupture of a few of the fibres. The result is pain which can be intense, swelling which comes up within a few minutes, and bruising sometimes well up the leg. Cold compresses, or alternate hot and cold bathing are emergency measures, but as soon as possible it should receive medical attention. In a severe case there is always the chance of a small fracture of the lower end of the fibula, or of the 5th metatarsal bone, for which reason no doubt the doctor in charge would secure an x-ray. A fracture, if present, would delay return to work but would not leave any permanent damage. The ankle is a good healer and the victim of this injury need not feel that it will not be as good as ever in a relatively short time. The usual treatment consists in strapping from forefoot well up the leg and encouraging the owner to go about life as usual, adding possibly some form of physiotherapy later on. To any exercises which may be given at the clinic, the dancer can add with advantage those of her own which use the joint fully without weight-bearing, such as *battements frappés*, and *battements tendus;* and a few days later gentle *relevés, demi-pliés* and so on. As soon as possible a return to class is advisable, but, *pointe* work should be omitted until all swelling has disappeared. The sufferer from this injury may take comfort from the fact that for any residue of pain that may persist, there is no better treatment for it than a good session at the *barre.*

The actual bones of the feet rarely figure on the casualty list but yet the author has come across two cases which would be considered rare, one in a girl of twelve years old and another of fourteen. There is such a thing as a spontaneous fracture of one of the long bones of the forefoot, arising from no known cause and presenting as symptoms pain and swelling over the front of the foot. It cannot of course be treated except by the doctor and may keep the child off work for a month or more, but eventually training can be continued without any after effects.

One other minor condition that occurs occasionally is an extra growth of bone at the back of the heel. The heel becomes red and a soft bursa may form from the friction of the shoe. Indeed the whole condition may be caused by just that, so that it is important to examine all the footwear in use, including ballet shoes and the exact place the ribbons contact the heel when tied. With the relief of all pressure, including a protective pad if necessary, the swelling may subside, but otherwise the exostosis as it is called may have to be dealt with surgically.

Finally come complaints of pressure pain under the heel, or under the big toe. It may be caused merely by a hard ballet shoe and this should be investigated first. It is especially bad for a hard ridge of the shoe to be allowed to press into the soft flesh under the ball of the foot, as in an extreme case inflammation of the sesamoid bones embedded in the tendon of the muscles can be set up. These small bones do not become fully hardened until well on in the teens, and inflammation in them can be difficult to cure and result in leaving the foot unsuitable for training. This is a rare occurrence but not unknown.

Eliminating this source we come to the pain which is the precurser of the occupational hazard of the ballet dancer, *hallux valgus*. The first symptom may be pain on the under side of the big toe or on the outer, either on standing and especially when on the *half-pointe*. The immediate question that arises, as has already been stressed in the last chapter, is not about the toe but about the shoes in use. For ballet children more than any it is of paramount importance that all footwear should leave room for *all* the toes. The slightest shortening is sufficient to start off this trouble, the slightest lack of width at the toe end is enough to press the big toe towards the centre of the foot. Appearance is of secondary importance to the urgent necessity that there should be room for the toes to grow in the natural direction, with no pressure on any, especially on the big toe. And socks or stockings must be equally carefully watched. Two or three months' growth in a young child may necessitate replacements for both, and no economic reasons must stand in the way, hard though it may be. This is the first investigation to be made when a child complains of pain under or around the big toe joint, remembering that boys are no less immune from this trouble than girls if wrongly shod. All shoes, outdoor, indoor, ballet and even bedroom slippers should be examined. A very early *hallux valgus* may correct itself when given foot space inside the shoes. At a later stage little can be done for it.

The shape of the foot undoubtedly has some bearing on the predisposition to *hallux valgus*. The dancers in illustration 18 who have escaped this trouble all have a broad front and toes of medium length forming a circular pattern on the floor. Their toes are also straight. One often finds in the early signs of pain around the big toe that the pupil has the very bad habit of curling her toes in *barre* exercises, a fault difficult to detect in shoes, but detrimental if persisted in, and a very bad introduction to *pointe* work, in which the straight big toe is of prime importance. The child with the highly arched foot and the one with little arch are both apt to cultivate this habit of clutching, the first because she cannot otherwise feel her toes and the second in the mistaken impression that it will improve the arch. The result is an imbalance in the pull of the two systems of muscles which preserve the straightness of the toes, and loss of that strength which is needed for both springs and *pointe* work. It is not unlikely that this has some bearing on the incidence of *hallux valgus* but whether or no, it should be checked as likely to lead to other troubles.

Once the big toe joint has become deflected it is impossible to cure but careful and correct technique is the best insurance against any progression of the condition. For early cases it is worth while trying the effect of wearing an appliance at night, obtainable at some shoe stores under the unattractive name of bunion springs, which by means of a slot for the big toe and an adjustable webbing round the forefoot, keeps the toe in a good position during sleep. This will not cure the condition but is sometimes successful in checking any increase. Nothing however is to be gained by wearing a rubber pad between the big toe and its neighbour. This is more likely to push the second toe out of alignment than influence the first, and claims made for it are quite fictitious. Other than this it is important to keep the joint entirely flexible and to remember that teen-agers, succumbing to the lure of fashion shoes with high heels which throw the weight of the body on to the front of the foot, and with narrow fronts which cramp the toes, are sacrificing the serviceability of their feet for allure, and giving every opportunity for the big toe to become a trouble maker.

One other difficulty with the big toe may be mentioned briefly, but it is less common than *hallux valgus* and the pain is felt almost exclusively on the *demi-pointe*. This is known as *hallux rigidus* and as its name implies, it is a stiffening of the joint due to some arthritic increase of growth in the bones. It does not occur in children. It is more painful in action than is the *valgus* deviation but does not increase with the same speed. A severe case would be obliged to give up dancing, but a *very* mild degree may be kept under with the aid of some form of heat treatment and the stoicism which is characteristic of the ballet dancer. Eventually it will defeat the bravest but there may be some years of work before this happens, and dancers are not apt to look too far ahead . . . which is perhaps fortunate!

Before leaving the subject of foot strains and the incidence of *hallux valgus* in particular, the oft-repeated warning must again be given against too early *pointe* work. Although the recognition of the danger is far more widely accepted than a few years ago, it is still possible to buy blocked shoes to fit a six-year-old and to find classes where they are allowed to wear them. It cannot be too strongly stressed that "*pointe*" work is the end result of slow and gradual training of the whole body, back, hips, thighs, legs, feet, co-ordination of movement and the "placing" of the body, so that the weight is lifted upwards off the feet, with straight knees, perfect balance, with a perfect *demi-pointe*, and without any tendency on the part of the feet to sickle either in or out. This moment will arrive at different times for different children, not only by virtue of previous training but according to their physical type, and in this may be included the growth of the bones. All the bones of the body begin as a relatively soft material known as cartilage which becomes progressively ossified into true bone at different times, being completed as late as twenty-five years. During this period there is a gradual hardening from the centre outward. In the long bones, such as those of the leg, forefoot and toes, the shaft ossifies first, the ends known as the epiphyses remaining connected to the shaft only by cartilage until the early teens (figures 24, 25, 26), with considerable variation as between one child and another as to the exact time at which the cartilage becomes bony. Ideally, if *pointe* work could be delayed until this time in children with poor bone structure, no doubt their feet would be safeguarded, but as this is a counsel of perfection, the most that can be done is to prepare the whole body as perfectly as possible, and to ensure that the introduction of the work on *pointe* is slow and gradual, in no case earlier than twelve years of age and preferably later. The fact that some feet can be found to have survived the abuse of tottering around on blocked shoes from the age of six onwards is no criterion as to its safety. The author has met at least one case of a child whose strong feet were unharmed by "dancing" on *pointe* at six years old, but who succumbed with knee trouble. There is little doubt that the strain had been resisted by the feet but had been transferred to the knee joints.

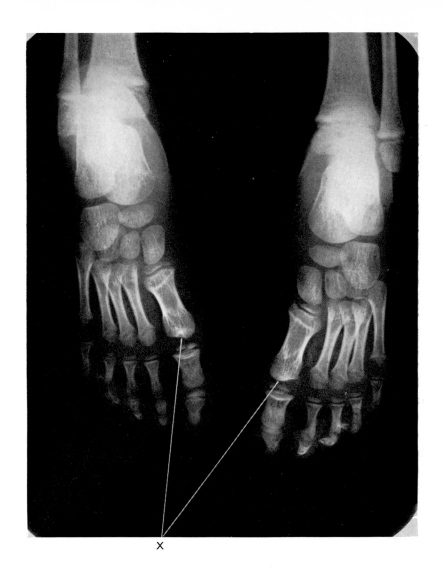

X

FIGURE 24

An X-ray of 4 year old feet. X Note the big space filled with soft cartilage between the bones of the forefoot and those of the toes; and the epiphyses of the bones of the toes, appearing as flat discs and separated from the main shaft.

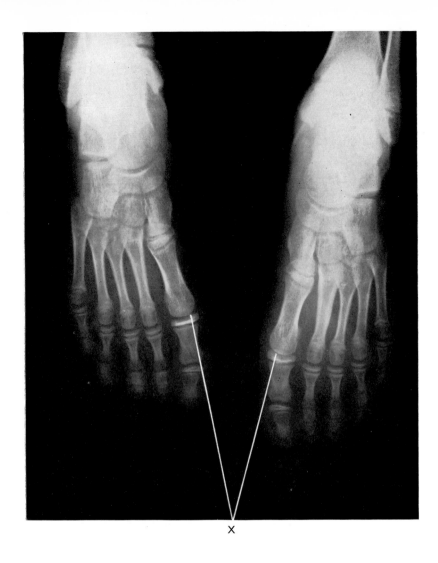

X

FIGURE 25

Feet at 11 years. X Note the forefoot bones are now less widely separated from the toes, but the epiphyses are still not joined to the shaft of the bones of the toes.

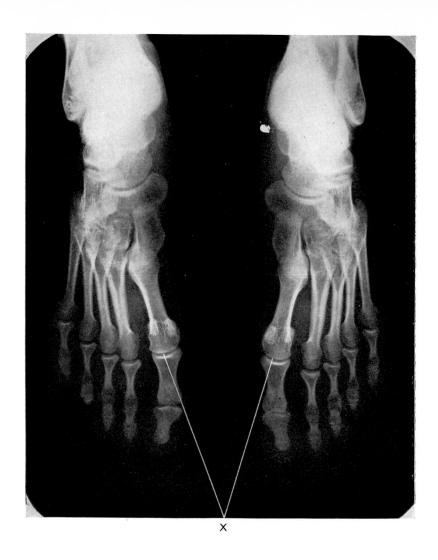

X

FIGURE 26

Feet at 19 years. X The bones of the toes are now in one piece and the space between the forefoot and toe bones is finally reduced. (Note also in this illustration there is a small degree of *hallux valgus*, showing the typical displacement of the upper end of the first metatarsal bone.)

THE KNEES

As has been said earlier, knees are second only to feet as a source of trouble. They have a tremendous amount of hard work from the very beginning. They are vulnerable and unforgiving joints. An ankle will recover from quite severe injury with no after-effects but the knee has a long memory and any real damage to it can be a major calamity.

Injuries or inflammatory conditions fall roughly into two classes, those which affect the ligaments and cartilages and those in which the patella is involved. The former are the most common and the earliest complaints come from the very junior children and are usually due to nothing more than an excess of zeal in pulling up the thighs, which action of course draws up the patella. The resulting pain may be well above the knee or just below (figure 27) and is caused by a slight stretch on the tendon of the muscle on the front of the thigh which pulls up the patella, or upon the ligament by which the patella is attached to the tibia below. It is as well to give the child a day or two off work, when the pain should disappear, and a warning to avoid any jerking in straightening the knees when back at the *barre*.

Apart from this small strain, others depend very largely on the formation of the knees in relation to the thigh and leg. A knee which is in good alignment rarely gives any trouble. By far the greater number of troubles occur amongst those pupils with any marked

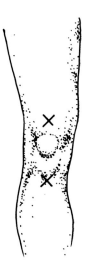

FIGURE 27. SITE OF PAIN DUE TO "PULLING UP" THIGH MUSCLES TOO FORCIBLY.

degree of knock-knee, those with short hamstring muscles who there-fore do not straighten the joint without effort and definitely those with any hyperextension or sway-back at the knee joint. In the first of these, the knock-kneed, there is often some laxness in the joint, with resulting instability and a lack of a perfect balance in the working of muscles and ligaments on either side which control and produce movement. In addition, the tibia is slightly out-turned, rendering it easy for the child to turn out from below the knee instead of from the hip, a fruitful source both of foot and knee strain.

Most complaints may be given a day or two off work and perhaps strapped or bandaged before returning to the *barre*, but when a child points definitely to the inner or outer side of the knee as the pain-giving spot it is a signal for caution. The inner side especially is the most commonly met site of strain of the lateral ligament, and later of a nipping or displaced cartilage. Before thinking so far ahead, however, it is wise to make sure that the cause does not lie nearer at hand, in fact at the first exercise at the *barre*. *Pliés* are a tax on the knee even when perfectly performed, more especially in the upward movement. Any falling inwards of the knees at the moment of rising puts a great strain on the inner side of the joints and this is doubled when there is any relaxation or "sitting" at the lowest point. This fault is injurious to the feet, but much more so to the knees and, repeated continually, may easily be the source of strain on the ligaments. The immediate treatment for any complaint therefore in this region is a few days' rest and, as usual, correction of any mistakes in technique. Persistence in the pain calls for medical investigation.

In neither of these strains do we find swelling, but in a third condition the knee is puffy and stiff, due to inflammation in the bursa or sac of fluid which acts as a buffer between the patella and the tibia. It is more likely to be the result of a blow or prolonged kneeling than from straight work, and if it does not subside speedily with kaolin poultices or similar treatment advice should be obtained with-out further delay.

Any condition in which a knee locks should be regarded as needing immediate investigation, as also should that in which it gives way suddenly. Either may recover temporarily, but should never-theless be taken as warnings, and the possibility be eliminated of a cartilage nipping or a patella slipping. Pain which is felt either over or under the patella, more when the knee is flexed than when straight, needs an accurate diagnosis of the cause for fear of inflammation of the under surface of the patella, a condition which if it exists would be likely to put an end to further training. One cannot say why this arises, other than over-use of a joint predisposed to such a condition, perhaps by former injury which has not been divulged at the time of the audition. Parents and children are apt to forget the incidence of an accident in early years, or maybe have a reluctance to confess to such. Remember too that any infective illness may leave potential joint trouble, which might not become manifest under ordinary life conditions, but which will be awakened by the unusual demands of ballet. This is especially so in the case of the knee joint. These are rare eventualities in children, fortunately, but they do occasionally occur, again more often in the knee which is not in perfect alignment with the thigh.

THE THIGH

The next area of trouble is not in a joint but in the muscles on the inner side of the thigh (figure 28), caused by the stretch that is required of them in all movements *à la seconde*. There is a corresponding pain recognised as "rider's strain" due to a similar pull. In dancers it may become very persistent and is found in quite young pupils as well as in the seasoned. There is no better method of invoking

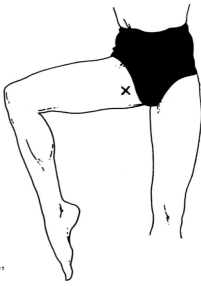

FIGURE 28. SITE OF "RIDER'S STRAIN"

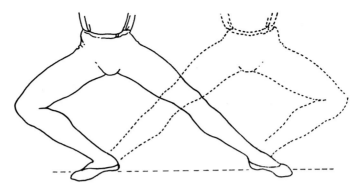

FIGURE 29. EASIEST POSITION FOR STRETCHING EXERCISE IN "RIDER'S STRAIN"

it than rushing to the *barre* and practising limbering exercises with leg raised on the *barre* before the lesson, instead of when the body is thoroughly warmed up. It can, however, arise without this culpable behaviour. It is caused by a few fibres of the muscle concerned having been overstretched or possibly torn at some time, and in the healing process they have become, as it were, matted together. They need therefore to be separated again and there are various treatments advocated to this end. Before resorting to them it is worth while trying self-help in the form of exercises which put a stretch on the painful spot. Thorough warming first is essential, either by a hot bath or by local heat. The victim should then put herself in a position when the pain is just noticeable and from this perform *gently* and *rhythmically* stretching movements to the limit of endurance. Such a position might well be one in which the leg is raised in second position on a low *barre* and the supporting leg bent and stretched alternately to get a further stretch on the painful thigh. Or the exercise could begin in a lunge position, both feet on the floor, swinging from side to side by bending the knees alternately; but the most favourable position can often be found by the performer. The essence of this cure . . . and it is astonishingly efficacious . . . is slow rhythmic movement, and persistence in spite of a temporary increase of pain and in spite of its intensity over a period varying from a few days to a month. The author has found it remarkably effective even in pain of long standing for which much more serious measures have been advocated. For adults a preliminary few minutes of very deep massage before the stretching may speed the cure but in children it is not necessary.

This pain is quite distinct from a catch or click which besets some students in the mid or later teens in performing the unfolding of the leg in *developpés* and which is confined almost exclusively to that movement, is felt in the groin but is sometimes referred to the region of the hip, though not in fact affecting the hip joint itself. Its exact cause is difficult to determine, but it wears off in time and though uncomfortable need not cause the dancer any concern.

THE HIP AND BACK

The hip joint as such is peculiarly free from trouble in spite of the abnormal work that falls upon it in ballet, but the lower back may have its quota. One does not meet complaints of pain in this region until well on in the teens, providing the structure of the body is normal and well proportioned. Those most prone to aches or pains are those with long backs and the tight hips which often go with them, as was pointed out in the previous chapter. Boys of this build may find lifts responsible for some discomfort if not definite pain, and in both girls and boys of an earlier age the effort to achieve a high *arabesque* or long holdings in *adagio, arabesques, attitudes* and their variants may be the starting point of pressure between the lumbar vertebrae. The strain may be transferred to the sacro-iliac joints, that meeting place of the last lumbar vertebrae and the pelvic bone known as the ilium. (figure 30.) Unless the pain is disabling a few days' rest can be allowed to see if it will disappear, and then any fault in the "placing" of the body carefully checked. It may be that the dancer is holding the upper part too vertical in *grands battements derrière* at the *barre* and in other exercises in fourth position *derrière en l'air*, or striving for greater flexibility than the type of back will allow. Boys may need some special strengthening exercises for the shoulders before continuing with "lifts". Or it may be that the dancer is overtired and needs rest. The spine is apt to register this need more quickly than any other part of the body.

Treatment for any pain in the back which does not recover quickly must be left to doctor, osteopath or physiotherapist, as the case may be. It is not wise to ignore it, but very necessary to correct any technical faults that may have produced it.

We have covered some of the aches and pains that are typical in the training of the dancer. That there will always be others is inevitable in combining the complexity of the human body with the complexity of ballet technique. But as has already been stressed, the closer the physique conforms to the ideal, the less the hazard of

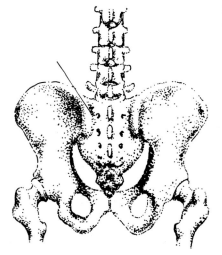

FIGURE 30. BACK VIEW OF PELVIS
AND SITE OF SACRO-ILIAC PAIN

strain in any part. Thorough warming up, perfect execution of *barre* work and good food rank high amongst insurance against injuries. All three are sometimes neglected. Nothing starts the circulation of the whole body more quickly than *pliés* at the *barre*, performed with meticulous care and concentration, yet it is not unknown for the boredom of endless repetition to creep in as the years go by, and for these most fundamental exercises to be done with the minimum instead of the maximum effort. It is also not unknown for a late comer to the class to do a few perfunctory exercises at the *barre* and then join in at a stage when the body ought to be thoroughly warm; and to perform the simplest limbering or stretching from cold is begging for trouble.

Correct execution, the second safeguard, can only come by degrees, but certain subtle errors can be checked from the very beginning. The troubles that may arise from the rolling or sickling foot have already been mentioned, as those also from the inturned hip, the straining for height rather than line in *adage* and so on. There is another technical fault which is common and often overlooked, viz. the habit of keeping the weight entirely on the supporting foot during the *barre* exercises. The failure to relax the muscles by transferring the weight on to *both* feet in that momentary pause between one movement and the next is a factor in muscles becoming bulky, hard and inelastic—and so liable to injury—and it is one of the nuances in the teaching that can easily be overlooked. The alternation of stretching and relaxing in muscular action is the greatest of all safeguards against strain and it is beautifully exemplified in ballet technique when correctly performed. Apart from increasing the bulk, it is possible that the bad habit of omitting the momentary relaxation between movements may also be the cause of cramp to which some pupils are prone—in the foot muscles and in the thighs. For them especially it is worth checking up on this point.

Tension and anxiety also play their part in muscle contraction, and perhaps the first essential here is to make sure that both are absent in the teacher. Nothing is more contagious than tension, except perhaps a relaxed yet authoritative presence in the person conducting the class.

Good food, the third on our list of preventives, raises the problem of the teen-ager who puts on weight and girth, to combat which she is afraid of her naturally good appetite and begins to diet. To tell her at this stage that she will thin down again later is no comfort. She persists in her fasting, loses weight and energy and finds she is not as strong on her *pointes* as she used to be, or that her back aches or that she has a pain here and another one there and goes off for various treatments when what she is needing is nourishment.* Naturally the diet for a dancer must be arranged with certain reservations, stodgy puddings eliminated in favour of fruit and salads, the intake of sugar, starches and fats modified, but any serious dieting should only be undertaken under medical supervision, and it is rarely necessary. A sudden and definite increase of bulk in the early teens may often be counteracted by cutting off one or even two classes a week, giving muscles which are overloaded with fatigue products the opportunity to eliminate them. Indeed, for more reasons than one it might possibly be of advantage if the training could be slowed down during the years between say fourteen and sixteen, when the changes of adolescence and the pressure of general education are making great demands on the physical and nervous system of the child. The increase of energy and vitality after this age is very noticeable in the ballet classroom and one wonders whether anything would ultimately be lost if a somewhat less intensive training were to precede it. The long slow building up of the body until it attains the strength, endurance, flexibility, speed, the refinement and the beauty which we almost take for granted in the tremendous technique of the ballet dancer is both a science and an art. It cannot be hurried—and it is never finished. The work for perfection has no ending even for the greatest ballerina—nor for that

* It may be noted that this state of affairs is not confined to teen-agers.

background figure, the teacher. Neither is the quest for knowledge ever completed for those who are called upon to make the momentous decision as to whether or no a child of ten should start out on that long road from classroom to stage. Of this nobody is more conscious than the author of this book.